The Big Bible Activity Book

Bethan James and Paula Doherty

A wonderful world

A long time ago, in the very beginning, God made a beautiful world.

God made light to shine in the darkness. He shaped the earth into mountains and valleys and filled them with towering trees and fruitful plants.

God filled the rivers and seas with fish and other creatures, and the skies with birds of every kind. God made animals, great and small, to live on the land.

God made people, man and woman, Adam and Eve, to take care of the earth and to be his friends.

Of the animals opposite which is the slowest?

Which animal has horns?

Which animal lives in a hole?

Which animal is best at swinging in trees?

Which animal runs very fast?

Which cheetah has the most spots?

d

Which cheetah has the biggest nose?

C

Which cheetah has the shortest tail?

b

Which cheetah has the shortest whiskers?

A

a

b

c

d

3

Noah's ark

'There's going to be a flood,' said God to Noah one day. 'Build an ark that will float on the waters so you can save your family and all the animals.'

So Noah built the ark and collected two of every kind of creature that lived on the earth, male and female. Then it rained for forty days and forty nights. Everything was washed away except Noah's ark.

When the water had dried up, Noah, his family and all the animals came out to see a beautiful rainbow; and Noah thanked God for keeping them all safe.

Which of these images matches the Noah in the big picture below?

a
b
c
d

b

4

Draw a line connecting each animal to a matching silhouette.

Abraham's long journey

When God asked Abraham to trust him, Abraham did.

Abraham travelled to Canaan, the place God said would be his new home.

When God told Abraham he and Sarah would have a huge family, Abraham believed God.

'Look at the stars in the sky, Abraham,' said God. 'Can you count them? That's how many descendants you will have.'

Abraham believed God even though many years passed and he and his wife grew old. And then Abraham and Sarah had baby Isaac, the beginning of his huge family.

Canaan

a   b   c

Which road leads to Canaan?

How many mice can you find in the big picture?

  How many rabbits can you find in the big picture?

  How many dogs can you find in the big picture?

True (✔) or false (✗)?
When God asked Abraham to trust him, Abraham did.

Where do these things fit in the big picture?

1 ☐   2 ☐   3 ☐   4 ☐   5 ☐

Esau and Jacob

Esau and Jacob were Isaac's twin sons.

When Isaac grew to be very old and he couldn't see very well, Jacob, the younger twin, played a trick on him. He brought Isaac a bowl of his favourite food — and dressed up as his older, hairier brother!

'Here you are, Father,' said Jacob.

'Is it really you, Esau?' said Isaac.

'Don't I feel like Esau? Don't I smell like Esau?' said Jacob.

'God bless you, my son, to lead my family when I am gone,' said Isaac.

Jacob was his mother's favourite son so Rebekah was very pleased. But when Esau found out — he was furious!!

Jacob's favourite son

Jacob married and had a very big family of his own – but he loved Joseph best of all.

'Joseph thinks he is better than all of us,' his brothers said. They didn't like Joseph at all.

Then one day, Joseph came to visit them as they looked after their father's sheep.

'Let's throw him in this well,' they agreed.

They told their father that Joseph had been eaten by a wild animal. But secretly they sold Joseph to some spice traders to be a slave in Egypt.

How many of Joseph's brothers can you see in the picture?

Which is the smallest sheep?

Which is the largest sheep?

a

b

c

d

e

f

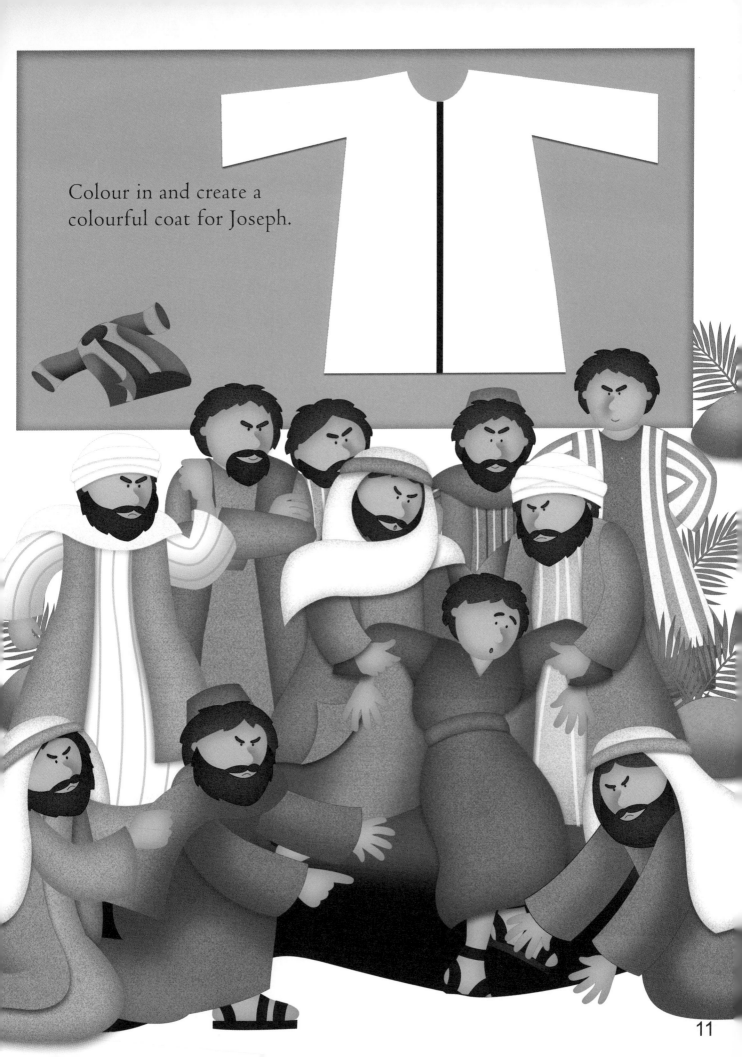

Colour in and create a
colourful coat for Joseph.

God takes care of Joseph

God did not forget Joseph.

One night the king dreamed strange dreams about corn and cows – and Joseph helped him to understand what his dreams meant.

'We must save lots of corn,' said Joseph, 'to stop us being hungry when the corn doesn't grow.'

The king was very pleased with Joseph and made him a very important man. When Joseph's brothers came to Egypt to buy corn, they didn't recognise their little brother who looked like an Egyptian. But Joseph recognised them!

'I know you wanted to hurt me,' he told them. 'But God was taking care of us all the time. Now we can all live in Egypt where there is plenty to eat.'

Which man is Joseph?

Which man is Joseph's father Jacob?

Which brother is wearing a green coat?

Which brother is wearing a red hat?

Who is wearing a blue and white robe?

Which brother has the smallest beard?

The princess and the baby

There was a cruel king in Egypt when baby Moses was born. First he made the Israelites his slaves. Then he told his soldiers to throw all their baby boys into the River Nile to drown them!

Moses' mother made a waterproof basket and hid him inside it. She put him by the reeds along the riverbank and told big sister Miriam to watch him secretly.

When the princess came to the river to bathe, she found baby Moses.

'I want to keep him!' she said.

So Moses was kept safe from the cruel king. God had a special job for him to do when he was grown up.

Draw a line to connect the right name to the right person.

Miriam

The Princess

Mother of Moses

A servant

Plagues in Egypt

Moses grew up to be a wise leader who loved God.

One day, God spoke to Moses from a burning bush.

'Tell the cruel king to let my people go free,' said God.

'I don't know your God,' said the king. 'I will not let these people go free.'

Then some horrible things happened. There were plagues in the land of Egypt.

'Now will you let my people go?' Moses asked the king.

'Yes!' said the king. 'Take your people and never come back!'

At last, Moses led God's people safely out of Egypt.

Can you copy this picture?

Can you guess what some of the plagues were?

Ladybirds or locusts?

Snow or hail?

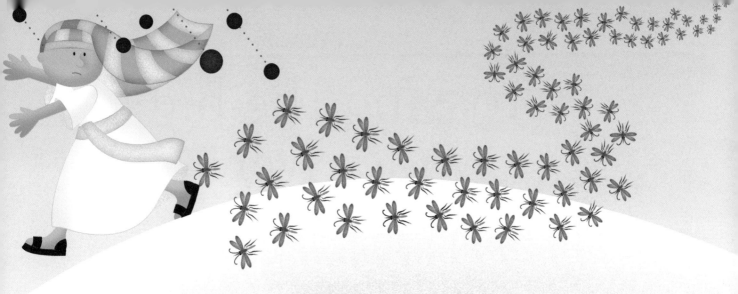

Find five differences between the pictures below.

Frogs or beetles? [ ]

Bees or flies? [ ]

Crossing the big, wide river

God led Moses and his people to the banks of the Red Sea. It was deep and wide and the people did not know what to do.

But God helped them to cross the water. Moses lifted his wooden stick – and the wind blew the waves back so all the people could cross safely on the path through the sea.

Then God looked after them. There was special food called manna and quail meat when they were hungry. There was refreshing water from a rock to drink.

Then one day, Moses talked with God on top of a big mountain, and God gave him ten special rules to help people live together happily.

How many crabs are there on this page?

Connect each matching pair of fish in this box.
How many pairs of fish are there in this box?

Tick the two pictures of Moses that are exactly
the same.

1

2

3

David, the youngest son

Samuel was a great prophet.

'You must choose the next king,' said God to Samuel.

Seven of Jesse's sons stood in front of Samuel, all tall and strong. It was hard to choose!

'Is it this one?' said Samuel. 'Or that one?'

'No, not this one,' said God. 'Nor that one.'

It was not one of Jesse's seven sons. But Jesse had another son, David, who was taking care of his father's sheep.

'David is good and wise,' said God. 'Choose him.'

Samuel sprinkled David with olive oil, as a sign that he would one day be king. God would always be there to help him.

Which two desks are a matching pair?

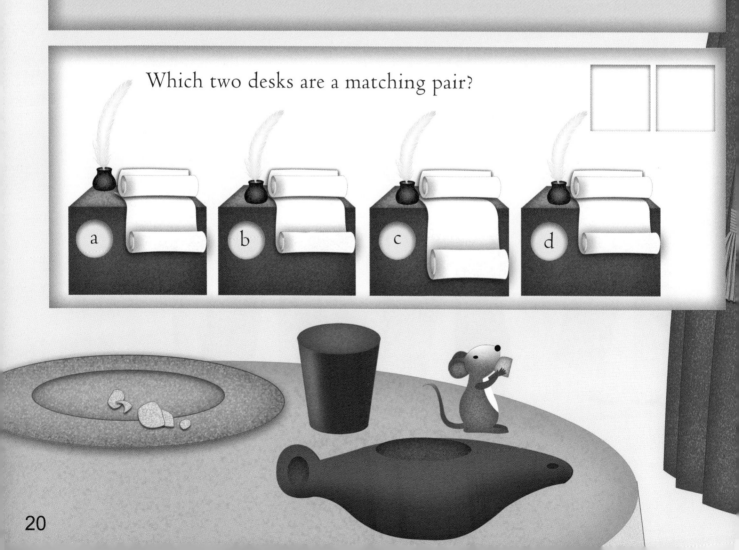

Tick the shapes that match the objects on the table opposite.

a

b

c

d

21

David and the giant

Goliath was fierce and bad and a giant of a man! King Saul's soldiers were too frightened to fight him.

'I'll do it,' said David bravely. 'God has helped me to fight lions and bears. He'll help me now.'

'YOU...?' roared Goliath. 'You're only a boy! And you're not even wearing armour!'

'But I come in God's name,' said David. He took five pebbles from a stream, and whirled one around in a sling.

Goliath toppled to the ground – and all his soldiers ran away. God had helped David defeat the giant.

Tick the correct statements and cross them if they are wrong.

There are more red soldiers than blue.

David took six pebbles for his sling.

God helped the giant to win the fight.

Elijah and the ravens

King Ahab worshipped a statue made of wood and stone. So God sent Elijah to warn him that until he worshipped the God who made all the world once more, there would be no rain on the earth. Then Elijah ran away to hide because the king was very angry!

God sent Elijah to a place where fresh water flowed in a little stream and big, black ravens brought food to him twice every day. Then a widow shared her last meal with him – and for as long as she shared, God made sure her oil and flour never ran out. God took care of Elijah – until rain fell on the earth once more.

Find four more lizards like this in the big picture.

Colour the birds black to finish the picture.

Jonah and the big fish

Jonah was running away. God wanted him to go to a place he didn't like with a message for people he thought were cruel and bad!

But Jonah had forgotten that you can't hide from God. A terrible storm blew up and Jonah's boat was tossed high on the waves.

'It's my fault!' Jonah told the sailors. 'Throw me into the water!'

Jonah called out to God to save him – and God sent a big fish to catch him. Three days later when God spoke to Jonah again, Jonah took God's message to the people – and they listened, and stopped being cruel and bad. Then God, who is kind and loving, forgave them.

Which Jonah is the odd one out?

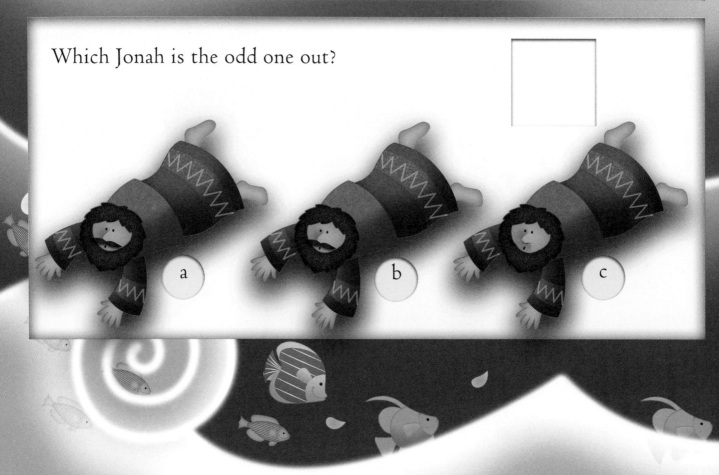

a   b   c

Which man was not in
the boat?

Daniel and the lions

Daniel worked for the king of Babylon. He loved God and prayed to him three times every day. But some jealous men told the king to make a new law. Anyone who did not worship the king should be thrown into a den of lions!

Daniel knew all about the new law, but he also knew that the king was just a man. He prayed to God just the same. And Daniel was thrown into the den of lions.

The king went to see what had happened the next morning.

'Don't worry, my King!' said Daniel. 'My God is able to save – even from the mouths of the lions, and he has kept me safe!'

These lions have lost their tails. Which tail fits which lion? Draw in the missing tails.

An angel visits Mary

A long time after Abraham, Isaac, Jacob and Joseph, God sent his Son to be born in the world. The angel Gabriel announced the news to a girl called Mary.

Mary gave birth to her baby in Bethlehem because she and Joseph had gone there to be counted in a census. She made a bed for him in a manger, because there was no room at the inn.

Find five things that are wrong with this picture.

How many animals are there in this picture?

Jesus is born

Outside Bethlehem, there were shepherds looking after their sheep.

'God's Son is born in Bethlehem!' the angels sang. 'He will be the Saviour of the world!' The shepherds ran to find him, the new-born baby Jesus! They knelt and worshipped him.

'God's angels sang to us,' they told Mary and Joseph. 'They told us where to find you.'

Mary listened to their story. Then the shepherds went back to their fields, praising God for what they had seen.

Find five differences
between this picture
and the one below.

Following the star

Far away in the east, some wise men saw a special star in the sky.

'It must be a sign from God,' they said.

'A new-born king,' they said.

'Let's travel to find him and take him presents,' they said.

The wise men followed the bright star until they found Mary and Jesus, her little boy.

The wise men knelt down and worshipped the baby. They gave him gold, frankincense and myrrh – very special gifts for a very special baby king.

How many camels can you see?

How many chickens?

How many animals altogether?

Can you draw a star here?

Jesus is baptised

Jesus grew up by Lake Galilee. He knew that God had a special job for him to do. He had been sent to show people how much God loved them. But he had also come to teach them how to live the way God wanted his people to live – kindly, fairly and generously.

First he went to the River Jordan where John was baptising people.

'But I can't baptise you,' said John. 'You don't need God's forgiveness.'

But Jesus knew it was what God wanted him to do. So John baptised Jesus. God was pleased.

Then Jesus chose twelve men to be his friends and learn from him. They were known as his disciples.

How many stones are in the water?

How many frogs can you see?

How many butterflies can you find?

God loves you

Jesus told the people stories to help them understand how much God loved them. He said God wanted them to be kind to each other – and to love their enemies and to pray for them.

'Say sorry if you hurt someone else; and forgive people if they hurt you.

'Share what you have with people in need; don't hide away all your money and keep it for yourself.

'Don't worry so much; God loves you and will take care of you. He is like a loving father – he will always be there, ready to welcome you when you need him.'

Put an 'o' under the oldest person. Put a 'y' under the youngest person.

How many children are in the picture?

How many adults are in the picture?

39

The hole in the roof

Jesus helped anyone who needed him.

He healed a man who couldn't walk when four friends brought him on a mat into a crowded house. They climbed on to the roof and made a hole big enough to lower their friend down!

Everyone was amazed when the man was healed. He picked up his mat – and walked home!

How many men can you find with beards in the big picture?

Number these characters as they appear left to right in the picture opposite so that the person on the far left is numbered 1, through to the person on the far right who should be numbered 6.

The storm on the lake

Jesus' disciples listened to everything he taught them. But they also saw that God had given him extraordinary power.

One evening, Jesus and his friends sailed across Lake Galilee.

The water rocked the boat gently and it had been such a busy day that Jesus soon fell asleep.

Suddenly a storm blew up and the wind lashed water into the boat. The men were tossed up and down till they felt sick.

'Wake up! Help us! We're going to drown!' they shouted to Jesus.

Jesus woke up and spoke to the wind and the waves. 'Be quiet! Be still!'

His friends were amazed as the storm went as quickly as it had come. Jesus had power over the wind and the waves.

How many disciples are in the boat?

Where do these puzzle pieces fit? Write the letter of the correct piece into the puzzle shape above.

Jairus' little girl

When Jairus came to see Jesus, he was very upset. His little daughter was very ill!

By the time Jesus arrived at the house, people were weeping and wailing. They said it was too late: Jairus' daughter had died. But Jesus took the hand of the little girl and spoke to her – and she opened her eyes.

'She'll be hungry,' said Jesus. 'She needs something to eat.'

Her parents were very, very happy. Jesus had healed her.

What are the five missing things in this picture?

How many adults are there in the room?

The very big picnic

There was a large crowd of people listening to Jesus. They loved the stories he told about God - but now they were hungry and far from home.

'Please take this,' a little boy said to James, one of Jesus' friends. In his hands were five little bread rolls and two little fish.

'Thank you,' said Jesus and, 'Thank you, God.'

Jesus' friends shared out the food – and everyone shared with each other. No one was hungry any more and there were twelve baskets of leftovers. It was a miracle.

Which of these children is not in the big picture below?

The man with no friends

Zacchaeus was a rich tax collector and a cheat. No one wanted to be his friend.

But Jesus was coming to Jericho where he lived and Zacchaeus wanted to see him very much. There was no room along the road so Zacchaeus climbed a tree and looked down – just as Jesus was looking up!

'Come down, Zacchaeus,' said Jesus. 'Let's eat together.'

Zacchaeus had never been so happy. Jesus was his friend.

'I'll give back all the money I stole,' he said. 'And I will give lots of my money to poor people, too.'

'That's why I am here,' said Jesus, 'to help people like Zacchaeus to be God's friends.'

Which Zaccheus is the same as the one above?

a   b   c

How many squirrels are hiding in the tree?

49

Riding on a donkey

Jesus had been travelling with his friends, teaching and healing, for about three years. The time for the Passover feast was drawing near. They went into Jerusalem for the celebrations.

People lined the streets when they saw Jesus coming, riding on a donkey.

'Hooray, here comes Jesus!' they shouted. 'Look, it's Jesus our king!'

They waved large palm branches and laid their cloaks on the ground.

The religious leaders did not like the way Jesus was so popular with the people. They began to plot his death...

Draw a line connecting the feet with the right head.

The last supper

Jesus met with his friends in an upstairs room.

'Let me wash your feet before we eat the Passover meal together,' Jesus said.

'But that's a servant's job!' said Peter.

'No, Peter, we can all take care of each other. I want you to show people that we love God by loving each other.'

Jesus knew that soon his friend Judas would betray him; Jesus knew that people would come to arrest him.

'Eat this bread,' said Jesus. 'Drink this wine. When you do this again, you will remember that my body was broken and my blood was shed for you.'

Where do these things fit into the picture above?

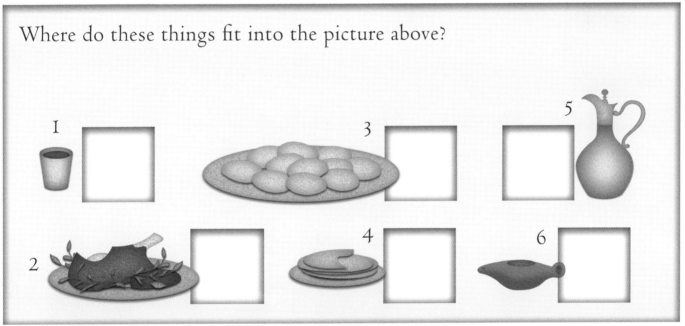

1

3

5

2

4

6

 Can you find four mice like this in the big picture?

Praying in the garden

After supper, Jesus' friends went with him to a quiet garden nearby. Jesus was sad. He was also afraid.

'Please help me to be brave, Father,' Jesus prayed. Meanwhile Jesus' friends fell asleep, one by one.

Suddenly his friends woke up! There were angry voices and swords and spears and bright lights coming into the garden... and there was Judas, leading the soldiers to Jesus, to take him to his enemies.

True or false? Tick the box if right. Put a cross if wrong.

This is Judas, a disciple of Jesus. ☐

Judas helped the soldiers to arrest Jesus. ☐

Judas fell asleep in the garden. ☐

Where do these puzzle pieces fit? Write the letter of the correct pieces into the puzzle shape above.

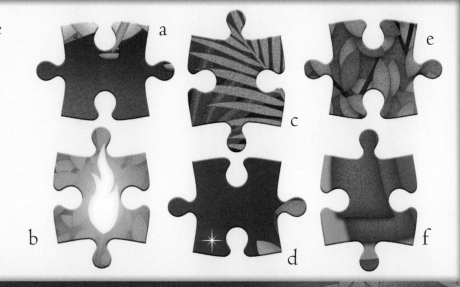

54

Jesus dies on a cross

Pontius Pilate, the Roman governor, knew Jesus was an innocent man but the crowd had been persuaded to ask for his death. His enemies pushed a crown of thorns on his head and made him carry the huge, heavy cross up the hill. When Jesus stumbled, the soldiers made a man called Simon carry it for him.

'Please forgive them,' Jesus said to God as they nailed him to the cross.

Jesus died that day. Later some of his friends carried his body to a beautiful garden and buried him in a dark cave. They rolled a heavy stone door across the entrance so no one could get in.

Find five differences between the two pictures above.

How many men are escorting Jesus up the steps?

The empty tomb

When the women went to the tomb on Sunday morning with herbs and spices, the heavy stone door was rolled away – and the body was gone!

'Don't look for Jesus here – he is alive!' said an angel.

Peter and John came to see if what the women said was true. Then Mary Magdalene met Jesus in the garden! Jesus met the disciples, who were in a locked room. Later he met some of them again when they were in their boat. They all knew for certain that Jesus was alive.

'Go and help others become my disciples,' Jesus said.

Tick the shape that is the most like the stone that blocked the tomb entrance.

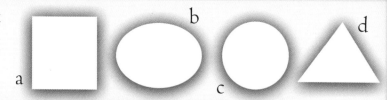

a   b   c   d

Tick the shape that is the same as Jesus in the picture opposite.

a   b   c

58

How many squirrels can you find on these two pages?

How many rabbits can you find on these two pages?

Breakfast by the lake

Peter and his friends had fished all night but they didn't catch any fish at all. Then just as the sun was rising, they heard a voice from the water's edge.

'Put your nets out on the other side of the boat!'

As soon as the nets filled with fish the friends knew it was Jesus. They shared a bread and fish breakfast with Jesus as he told them that soon he would return to God in heaven.

'I will send you the Holy Spirit so you will have power to tell everyone about God,' said Jesus. 'You will never be alone. I will always be with you.'

Can you find four things wrong with the boat?

How many baskets are in the boat?

Label the shapes below a, b or c to link them to the right disciple above and then link each pair of shapes with a line.

ANSWERS

Page 2 Which animal is the slowest? *d*
Which animal has horns? *b*
Which animal lives in a hole? *a*
Which animal is best at swinging in trees? *c*
Which animal runs very fast? *e*

Page 3 Which cheetah has the most spots? *d*
Which cheetah has the biggest nose? *c*
Which cheetah has the shortest tail? *b*
Which cheetah has the shortest whiskers? *a*

Page 4 Which of these images matches the Noah in the big picture below? *b*

Page 5 Draw a line connecting each animal to a matching silhouette.

Page 6 Which road leads to Canaan? *a*

Page 7 How many mice are in the big picture? *2*
How many rabbits are in the big picture? *4*
How many dogs are in the big picture? *1*
Did Abraham trust God? *True*

Page 8 Where do these things fit in the big picture?
1:*c*, 2:*a*, 3:*d*, 4:*b*, 5:*e*

Page 10 How many of Joseph's brothers can you see in the picture? *10*
Which is the smallest sheep? *c*
Which is the largest sheep? *f*

Page 13 Which man is Joseph? *m*
Which man is Joseph's father Jacob? *l*
Which brother is wearing a green coat? *f*
Which brother is wearing a red hat? *h*
Who is wearing a blue and white robe? *g*
Which brother has the smallest beard? *b*

Page 15 Draw a line to connect the right name to the right person.

Page 16 The plagues in Egypt were: *locusts, hail, frogs and flies.*

Page 17

Page 19 There are *4* crabs on the page.
There are *4* pairs of fish.

The pictures of Moses that are the same are: *1 and 2.*

Page 20 The two desks that are the same are: *b and d.*

Page 21 The two shapes that match the picture are: *c and d.*

Page 23 True or false
There are more red soldiers than blue: *True.*
David took six pebbles for his sling: *False.*
God helped the giant to win the fight: *False.*

Page 24

Page 26 Which Jonah is the odd one out? *c*

Page 27 Which man was not in the boat? *e*

Page 29 The correct tails are marked.

Page 30

Page 31 There are 14 animals in the picture.

Page 33

Page 35 How many camels can you see? *3*
How many chickens can you see? *4*
How many animals altogether? *11*

Page 37 How many stones are in the water? *7*
How many frogs can you see? *2*
How many butterflies can you find? *6*

Page 39

How many children are in the picture? *10*
How many adults are in the picture? *8*

Page 40 How many men can you find with beards? *11*
The characters appear in the order *2, 5, 4, 3, 6, 1*

Page 43 How many disciples are in the boat? *12*
The puzzle pieces go with these numbers: *1c, 2a, 3e, 4d, 5b, 6f*

Page 44

Page 45 How many adults are in the room? *6*

Page 47 Which of the children is not in the picture? *a*

Page 49 Which Zacchaeus is the same as the one in the picture? *b*
There are *3* squirrels in the tree.

Page 51

Page 53 Where do the things fit? *1a, 2f, 3d, 4c, 5b, 6e.*

Page 54 True or false?
This is Judas, a disciple of Jesus. *True*
Judas helped the soldiers to arrest Jesus. *True*
Judas fell asleep in the garden. *False*
The puzzle pieces fit in this order. *1e, 2d, 3b, 4a, 5c, 6f.*

Page 57

How many men are escorting Jesus up the steps? *4*

Page 58 Tick the shape most like the stone. *c*
Tick the shape most like Jesus. *a*

Page 59 How many squirrels are in the picture. *1*
How many rabbits are in the picture. *5*

Page 61

How many baskets are in the boat. *4*

First edition 2017
Copyright © 2017 Anno Domini Publishing
www.ad-publishing.com
Text copyright © 2017 Bethan James
Illustrations copyright © 2015 Paula Doherty

Published 2017 by Authentic Media Ltd
PO Box 6326, Bletchley, Milton Keynes, MK1 9GG, UK
www.authenticmedia.co.uk
ISBN: 978 1 86024 982 2
Conforms to EN71 and AS/NZS ISO 8124

Publishing Director: Annette Reynolds
Art Director: Gerald Rogers
Pre-production Manager: Doug Hewitt

Printed and bound in China